VIOLIN PLAYING

BOOK FOUR

ROBERT TRORY

*A comprehensive and contemporary tutor in five
books that guides the student from the very first
notes through to an advanced level.*

Published by

Waveney Music Publishing Ltd

© 2006

VIOLIN PLAYING

SERIES CONTENTS

Book One - introduces Finger Pattern No 1, including all four fingers, elementary one-octave major scales & arpeggios with rhythmic variations, detached bowing, slurring and crossing strings. There are many original violin duets throughout. Some of these are published separately with piano accompaniments by Sally Mays.
(This book covers the requirements for the Preparatory or Initial Grade Exam*.)

Book Two - introduces Finger Patterns No 2, No 3 & No 4, together with portato bowing, linked dotted bowing, extended scales, chromatics, minor scales, scales in broken thirds, elementary finger exercises, double stops and the general development of sound bowing. There are many original violin duets throughout. Some are published separately with piano accompaniments by Sally Mays.
(This book covers the requirements for Grade One and Two*.)

Book Three - introduces third position and second position, further development of scales & arpeggios and chromatics, together with martelato bowing and re-taking the bow.
(This book covers the requirements for Grades Three & Four*.)

Book Four - introduces fourth, fifth and sixth positions, the development of bowing techniques, including string crossing, staccato, spiccato and the use of the fingers on the bow, together with further chromatics, left hand stretches and general facility.
(This book covers the requirements for Grades Five, Six and much of Grade Seven*.)

Book Five - is a selection of essential studies that introduces playing in higher positions, tone production, more advanced string crossing, ricochet bowing, up bow staccato, and develops general facility.
(This book completes the requirements for Grade Seven and covers the requirements for Grade Eight*. It then leads on to the further study of the standard works of Kreutzer, Rode, Dont, Gaviniès and Alard amongst others, and to the contemporary work of Simon Fischer.)

* The Grade exams referred to are the practical examinations conducted in the UK, and in many other parts of the world, by the examining bodies of the Associated Board of the Royal Schools of Music and the joint Trinity College and Guildhall School of Music known as Trinity Guildhall.

Cover illustration 'The South Bank Fiddler' © John Barber 2006
Printed in England by Halstan & Co. Ltd., Amersham, Bucks.

ISBN   978-0-9554384-7-9

INTRODUCTION

I have set out to write a series of books that steadily builds the solid foundations required for a sound technique. The approach is thorough and is based on the best traditions of teaching the violin. It follows the format of scales, exercises and studies, together with enjoyable and musical pieces, and with a modern and attractive presentation.

The development of the left hand works through finger patterns that themselves are related to tonality or keys. From this the pupil understands the 'geography' of the violin and grows ever more confident as a consequence.

Many of the pieces are written or arranged for two violins so that music-making flows naturally and is easily accomplished. The playing of duets also promotes a confidence in the student and adds to the enjoyment of lessons.

Many of the pieces in Books One and Two have piano accompaniments available, expertly written by the pianist and composer Sally Mays, and are published separately.

As the student progresses through Books Three and Four an increasing amount of the rich repertoire written for violin and piano becomes available. The student will also, no doubt, be enjoying time spent in a youth orchestra.

Visit **www.violinplaying.com** for some repertoire suggestions.

Robert Trory 2007

*I wish to dedicate these books to my wife Nina
and to all my pupils without whom these
books would never have been written.*

For a full list of publications and free downloads
visit the website www.violinplaying.com

FOURTH POSITION - SHARP KEYS

When making the slide up on the second finger or when playing the scales exercise, keep the first finger on the string. The first finger is an 'anchor' that keeps the hand steady and in shape. Note that the interval between the second and third fingers changes.

Complete E major

Keep the first finger on the string through the position change.

Study

R. Trory

March

R. Trory

On Wings Of Song

(Using 1st, 2nd, 3rd & 4th positions)

F. Mendelssohn arr. R. Trory

Complete D minor

Study

R. Trory

Study

F. Wohlfahrt

Allegro Appassionata

F. Wohlfahrt arr. R. Trory

CROSSING STRINGS

In order to appreciate how little movement is required for the bow to change strings, try this exercise. Play the A and D strings together then, without moving the arm, simply drop the hand down from the wrist until the bow is only in contact with the A string. Raise the hand again until the bow is back on both strings then raise the hand further from the wrist, again not moving the arm, until the bow is only in contact with the D string. The bow hand should have described a shallow wave pattern.

Now repeat the exercise and exaggerate the movement so that the bow touches the E string and G string as well, but still without moving the arm. The bow hand will describe a more pronounced wave pattern.

Continue with the following exercises using only the wrist.

Study

Legato string crossing combining arm and wrist movement.

F. Wohlfahrt

Moderato

13

STACCATO AT THE HEEL

This bowing technique is easier to learn if the student has already prepared by practicing scales with all down bows, and is used to playing right at the heel of the bow.

The bow must be 'punched' into the string with contact made immediately under the index finger on the bow, with the full hair flat on the string. The index finger acts as a 'shock absorber' and prevents uncontrolled bouncing. However, the bow needs to be allowed to rebound off the string quite a long way, so the bow arm and fingers need to be relaxed at all times. The 'punch' is with arm weight only and not with muscle. Keeping the fingers relaxed and spongy will ensure that the bow remains on the string for just the right length of time to sound the note before rebounding. Any movement of the fingers of the bow hand is 'passive' or 'reactive' and is not made to happen.

This bowing feels quite different on each string due to the changing angle of the bow as it strikes the different strings. Take care to get used to the feel of each string in order to achieve a clean strike on each note.

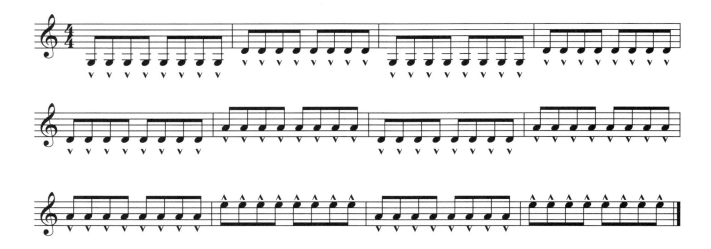

Practise scales with this bowing. As you go higher up the string, bring the bow closer to the bridge to avoid losing the 'bite' in the higher register.

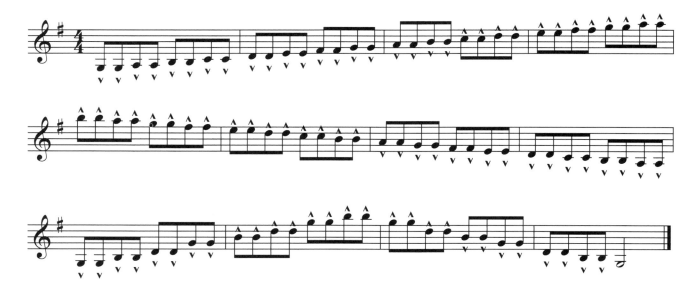

Study

Kayser Op.20 No.1

Scarey Staccato

Allegro

R. Trory

16

Position-changing exercise to 4th position.

Much of modern violin technique was developed by the Czech violinist and teacher, Ottakar Ševcík. His position-changing exercises are essential to a fluent left hand technique. Here is a preliminary study that immitates Ševcík's method. Always practise these exercises keeping all the fingers on the string whenever possible.

R. Trory

PORTAMENTO

The process of shifting from one position to another, gives rise to the possibility of portamento, a sliding between notes. The degree to which the slide is heard will always be governed by what the individual player regards as 'good taste', and fashions have changed, and will continue to change, from generation to generation. The effect of portamento helps the string instrument to come closer to the voice. Traditions will therefore vary from region to region as they are shaped by the principle singing traditions and languages of that region, and other ethnic influences. Portamento is prompted by the desire for greater expression and will therefore be governed by what the violinist believes to be appropriately expressive within the context of a certain piece of music or passage. When fingering a passage, therefore, one does what is necessary to produce one's personal desired effect.

'Same-finger' slides are universally applied, as there is no possible way in which one might be able to employ these differently. Also when sliding down it seems universally accepted that one slides on the initial note. However differences of opinion occur in the upward shifts.

If Rowsby Woof and Herbert Kinsey could be taken as being indicative of the 'English' school then the English method is quite clear. In all cases, one should slide on the initial note (the finger one is coming from) as opposed to the end note (the finger one is going to). In the examples below, they would advocate sliding on the first of the paired notes.

However, my own teachers, heavily influenced by a Central European and a largely Jewish heritage, insisted that when shifting on adjacent fingers, (1-2; 2-3; 3-4) one must slide on the end note finger. With non-adjacent fingers (1-3; 2-4; 1-4) one must slide on the initial note finger. For example......

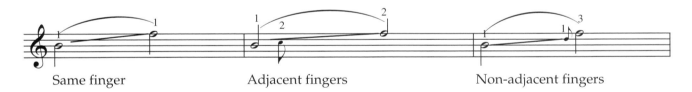

Same finger   Adjacent fingers   Non-adjacent fingers

The same principle applies to shifts that also involve a change of string.

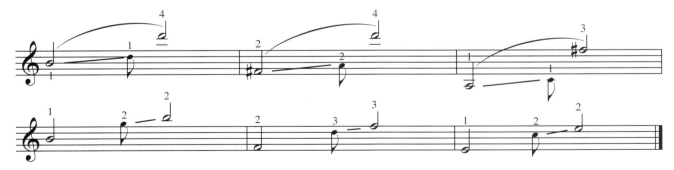

Having said all this, perhaps rules are there to be broken from time to time. Practise all the different ways of making a slide and then make your own choices as to where and when to use portamento.

Andante catabile

F. Wohlfahrt arr. R. Trory

FOURTH POSITION - FLAT KEYS

Complete Eb major

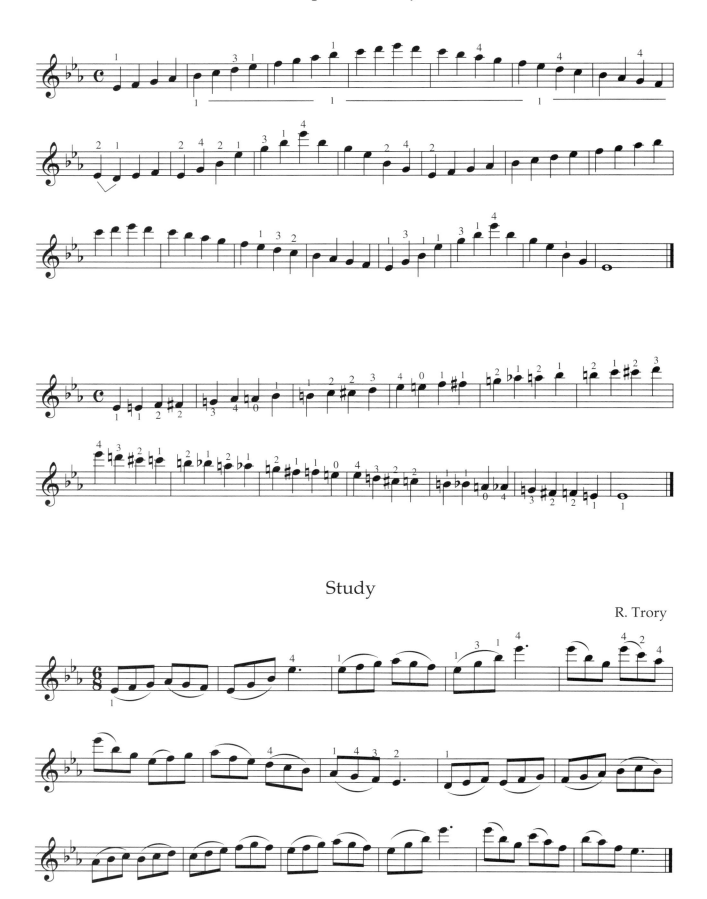

Study

R. Trory

Position-changing exercises to 4th position.

Here is another study in the style of Ševcík, this time in the flat key of Ab major. Always practise these exercises keeping all the fingers on the string whenever possible.

R.Trory

TWO CHROMATIC STUDIES

"The study of chromatics is too often neglected. Each note must stand out clearly, lest the whole series be mistaken for some variety of caterwauling. A quickness of physical movement of the fingers should be developed." So said Leopold Auer, the teacher of some of the most famous violinists of the 20th Century, among them Jasha Heifitz and Nathen Milstein. These studies by Wolfahrt would have been known to Auer.

F. Wohlfahrt

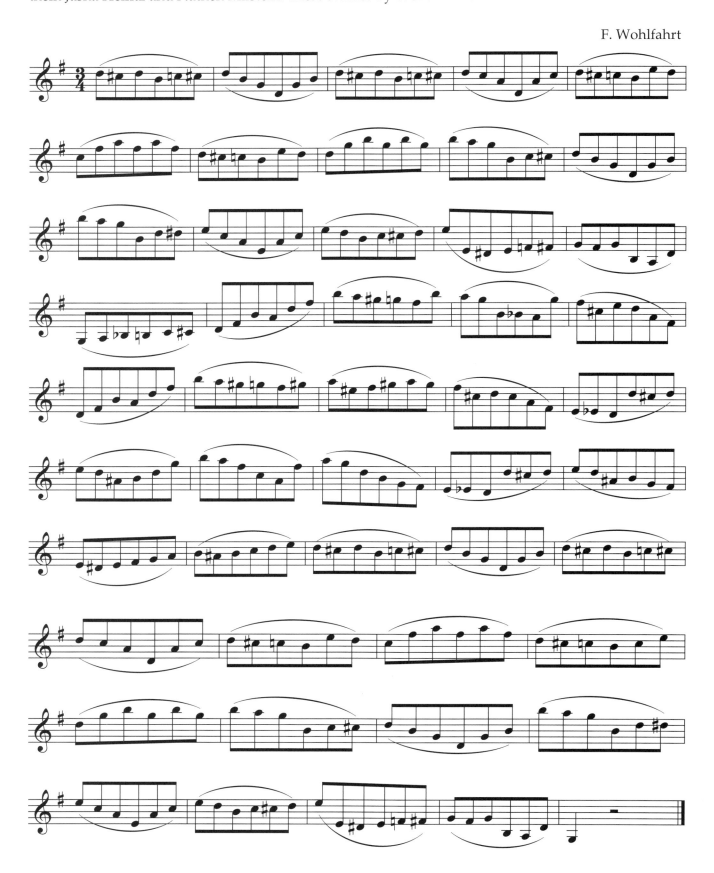

F. Wohlfahrt

27

Exercise for improving the stretch.

Keep the fingers on the string. Practise on all four strings.

R. Trory

Exercise to improve the independence of the fingers.

Keep all four fingers on the strings, both whilst playing the notes on the A string and when resting them on the E string. This exercise can be developed by playing the notes on the A string faster as quavers and eventually as a trill.

R. Trory

Here is another study from Franz Wohlfahrt that combines some chromatic fingering with fourth finger stretches. This study works the fingers in such a way that they will become strong *and* supple - an ideal combination.

F. Wohlfahrt

Finger Exercise

Developing the speed, strength and rhythm of the fingers is important. First practise some scales with the two different dotted rhythms. In the first rhythm, the fingers must be lifted very quickly and in the second, the fingers must be 'hammered' down. After practising scales like this, play the study with very rythmic fingers, starting at a moderate tempo and then gradually increasing the speed.

Study

R. Trory

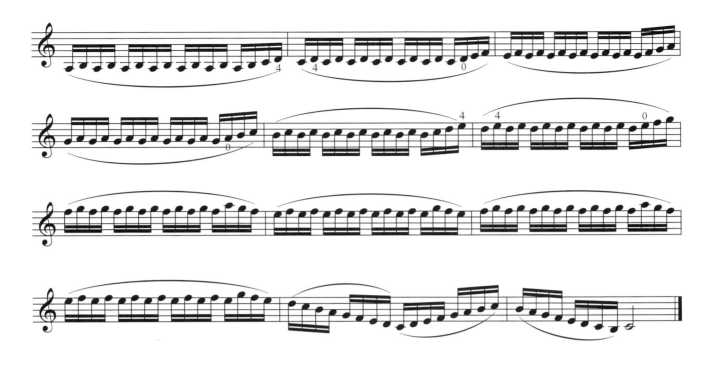

Scales for speed

Allegro Agitato

A study for the quickness of fingers and co-ordination of the bow.

F. Wohlfahrt arr. R. Trory

DOUBLE STOPPING EXERCISES

Melody

R. Trory

Cantabile

A study of 'Melodious Double Stops' Books One & Two by Josaphine Trott, published by Schirmer, and Ševcík's Op.9 Preparatory Double Stopping exercises, published by Bosworth, should commence here. The author considers it unnecessary to replicate the material in these works as he considers that they cannot be bettered.

FIFTH POSITION & THREE OCTAVE SCALES IN G MAJOR

Shifting to fifth position through third position.

Finger exercise on the E string.

G major three-octave scale.

G major three-octave broken thirds scale.

G major scale slurred in octaves.

Study

F. Wohlfahrt adapted R. Trory

Scales and Arpeggios on One String

Starting on an open string - first to fourth positions.

Starting on first finger in sharp keys.

Starting on first finger in flat keys.

Position-changing exercises to 5th position.

R. Trory

F major

F minor

Melodic

Harmonic

Complete F major

restez

restez

40

Träumerei

Robert Schumann arr. R. Trory

F♯ major

F♯ minor

Melodic

Harmonic

Complete F♯ major

Simple Gifts

5th pos (sempre restez)

Trad. arr. R. Trory

Romantische Stück Op.75 No.1

Allegro moderato

A. Dvorak arr. R. Trory

EXERCISE TO DEVELOP THE FINGERS OF THE BOW HAND

Some bowing techniques require the fingers of the bow hand to be 'passive' or 're-active' but some require the fingers to make well co-ordinated 'positive' or 'pro-active' movements.

Place the bow on the A string in the middle of the bow and without moving the arm or wrist, but using only the fingers, make a down bow and then an up bow. If difficulty is experienced in not moving the arm and/or wrist, then bring the left hand under the violin and hold the right wrist with the left hand.

When the single up bow and down bow is accomplished then split the movement into two parts so that there are two down bows and two up bows. Remember that the little finger must remain on the bow throughout, as well as the thumb remaining bent underneath.

LINKED BOWING WITH DOTTED RYHTHMS

This bowing technique was first learnt in Book Three and it was recommended that scales should be practised with this bowing on a regular basis. It is also used frequently in the Golliwog's Cakewalk.

Study

F. Wohlfahrt

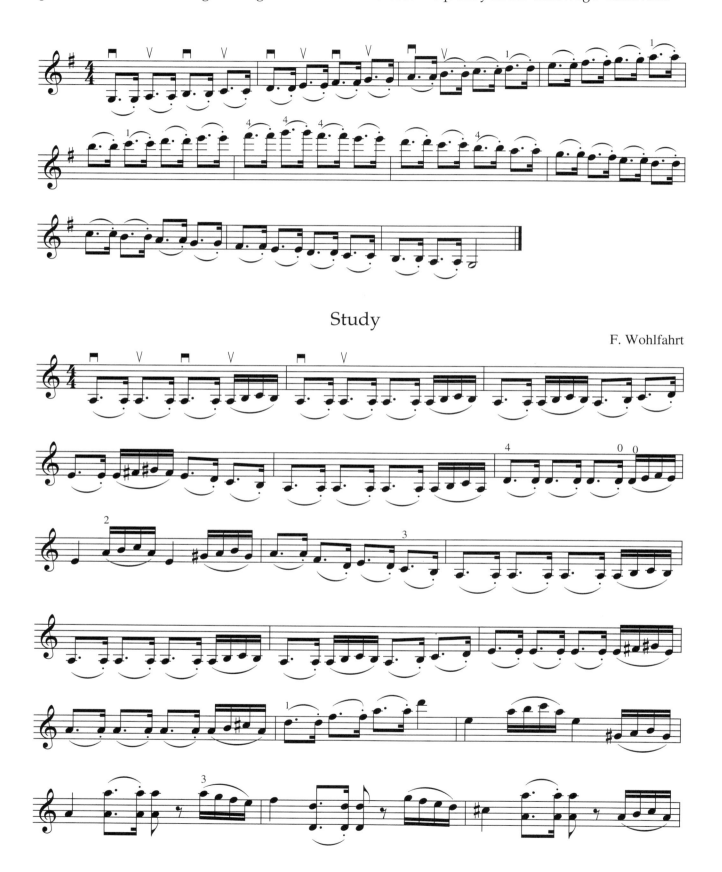

46

Golliwog's Cakewalk

Allegro giusto

C. Debussy arr. R. Trory

Un peu moins vite

Download a Second Violin part free at **www.violinplaying.com** and enjoy this as a violin duet.
Also available arranged for String Quartet.

SPICCATO & SAUTILLÉ BOWING

The student should now be able to play with a variety of different bow strokes.
Here is a list of all the bowing techniques to be learnt at this stage. Spiccato and sautillé are the last of these.

1. Détaché at varying speeds.

2. A smooth legato crossing strings.

3. Martelé - a marcato, on the string, at the point of the bow, requiring a sharp pressure of the index finger on the bow and quick arm movement.

4. Staccato at the heel. A 'hammered' or 'punched' bowing requiring the arm to be pro-active and the bow hand relaxed and re-active.

5. Re-taking the bow. This uses successive down bows, or successive up bows, requiring a re-take of the bow. The bow is balanced with the little finger of the bow hand when it is off the string. Don't try to control the bow with the arm.

6. Portato. Successive up bows, or down bows, without re-taking the bow.

7. Spiccato. The bow is like a ball. It wants to bounce naturally. In order to make a ball bounce up it is necessary to throw it down. The same applies to the bow. Don't try to lift the bow. Throw the bow down on to the string. The downward pressure of the arm weight will cause the bow to spring away from the string. The springing bow can be felt in the fingers of the bow hand. If they remain relaxed, they can react to this spring and control the balance and a continued bounce.

8. Sautillé. Very fast double notes played with light pressure in the middle of the bow, so that the bow jumps.

Exercises

First find out how your bow behaves when thrown onto the string. Every bow behaves differently. Answer these questions.
>   Where does it bounce best?
>   Where does it bounce fastest and slowest?
>   Does it behave differently on different strings?

Now develop a 'feel' for the bow bounce in the fingers of the bow hand, starting on open strings and then moving on through the simplest of scales. After a while it should be possible to start on the following studies and then incorporate the spiccato into pieces of music.

Spiccato and sautillé bowing is indicated by dots attached to the notes.

Study

R. Trory

Now practise this study with all the other bowings and be sure to add these bowings to your scale repertoire.

Staccato at the heel.

Martelé at the point.

Détaché at varying speeds.

Legato one or two bars per bow.

Sautillé.

Portato

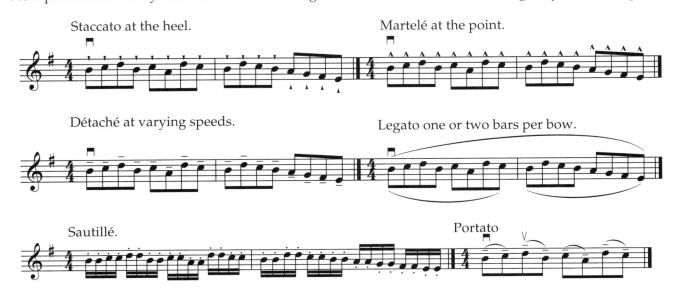

Hungarian Dance No.5

J. Brahms arr. R. Trory

SIXTH POSITION

Remember, when shifting on the second finger, keep the first finger down. Also note that the interval between the first and second fingers changes with each position change.

With this position changing exercise keep all the fingers down wherever possible so that the fingers learn the changing patterns.

Violin Playing Book 4

This workplan will consolidate technique and sight reading skills.

Pages	Aspect	Notes

Violin Playing Book 4   Index   Robert Trory

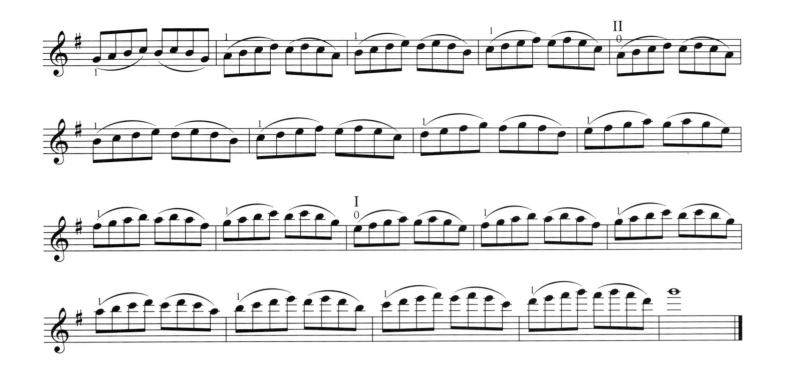

Study in Sixth Position

Rasposchol

Trad. arr. R. Trory